A DOG in the Big Courthouse

Written by Nicola Pearson

Illustrated by Maya Keegan

Layout & Graphic Design by Jon-Paul Verfaillie

Author's Note

I've known Ellen O'Neill-Stephens for many years and when her oldest son, Sean, was about to graduate from high school, she talked about wanting to find a way for him to continue to have social contact in his life outside his direct family. Since Sean is wheelchair bound and cannot speak, Ellen decided to obtain a service dog, Jeeter, to be his companion, whose presence in the community would draw friendly attention to Sean. Jeeter couldn't be with Sean all of the time, however, so Ellen, who was then a King County deputy prosecuting attorney, brought him to Drug Court with her so he could brighten up the lives of the teenagers trying to kick their drug addictions. Jeeter's presence at the courthouse had such a positive impact on nearly everyone he encountered that Ellen discussed the possibility of getting a full-time facility dog with Norm Maleng, the elected prosecutor, to help vulnerable people through the legal process. Initially he was reluctant to have a dog in the courthouse because he grew up on a farm where their dogs lived in the barn, but when Jeeter put his head on his lap, Norm instantly understood that he also needed a dog like Jeeter to become a member of his staff. In 2004, Ellie was the first official facility dog to work in the legal system. This inspired Courthouse Dogs Foundation, with Ellen O'Neill-Stephens at the helm, later joined by her friend and trained veterinarian, Celeste Walsen. These two ladies now travel the world, talking about the benefits of trained facility dogs in the courthouse, and inspiring people like me and Maya Keegan to write and illustrate a children's book for them.

ISBN-10: 0-9972804-4-1
ISBN-13: 978-0-9972804-4-9

Dedication

For Ellen and Celeste
and all the dogs who have loved me so freely.

~ N.P. ~

For Tia, Shadow, Cody, Allie, Riley,
and all the dogs that love unconditionally.

~ M.K. ~

For Madeline, Jarvis, Jessie,
and all the dogs.

~ J^2 ~

I asked my friend if she could be

Any creature in the world

What would she be, this friend to me,

Instead of being a girl?

"I think," she said, "I'd be a dog!

To live the life of Rover...

They play,

they sleep,

they
eat,

they love,

and then they do it over.”

"That's true," I said, my tone quite kind

(I didn't want to grouse)

COURTHOUSE DOGS® FOUNDATION

"But my grandma has a dog that works...

A dog in the big courthouse!"

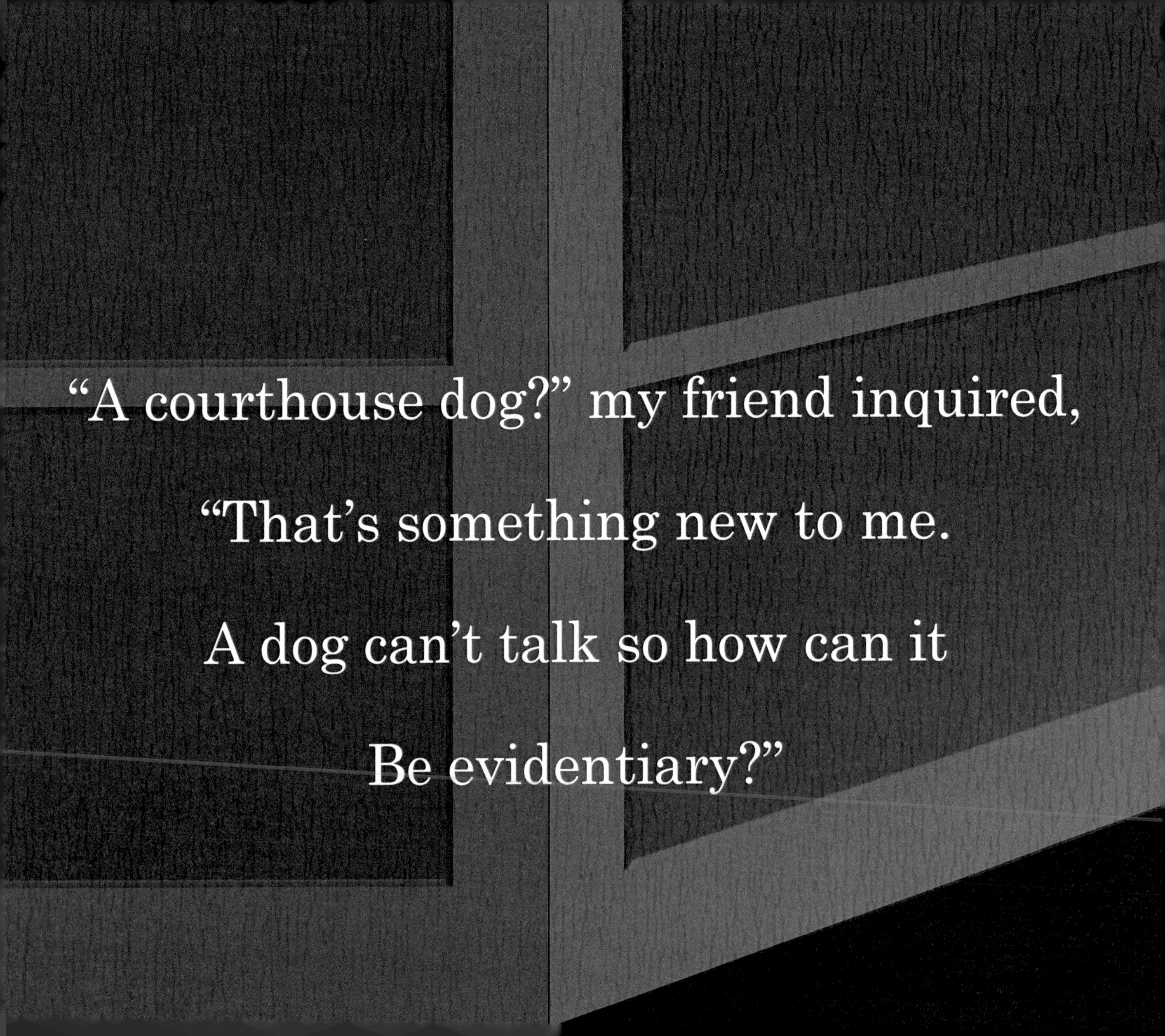

"A courthouse dog?" my friend inquired,

"That's something new to me.

A dog can't talk so how can it

Be evidentiary?"

A courthouse dog is trained for calm,

And helps when someone's scared

To say what really happened

Or to make the truth be shared.

PADS
ASSISTANCE DOG
PADS
ASSISTANCE DOG
PADS
ASSISTANCE DOG
PADS
ASSISTANCE DOG
PADS
ASSISTANCE DOG
PADS
ASSISTANCE DOG

My grandma's dog was purpose bred

A Lab, called Molly B,

She works in cases of high stress

That need neutrality.

Molly B supports by being there

When a witness needs a place

To say the things they have to say

And feel that they are safe.

My grandma knows about the law
She's had some special coaching
So she makes sure that Molly B
Will help without encroaching.

For courthouse dogs are strong like rocks,

Dependable and steady

They don't judge or take a side

They just get others ready.

And after work, Molly comes home

With Grandma, and we play...

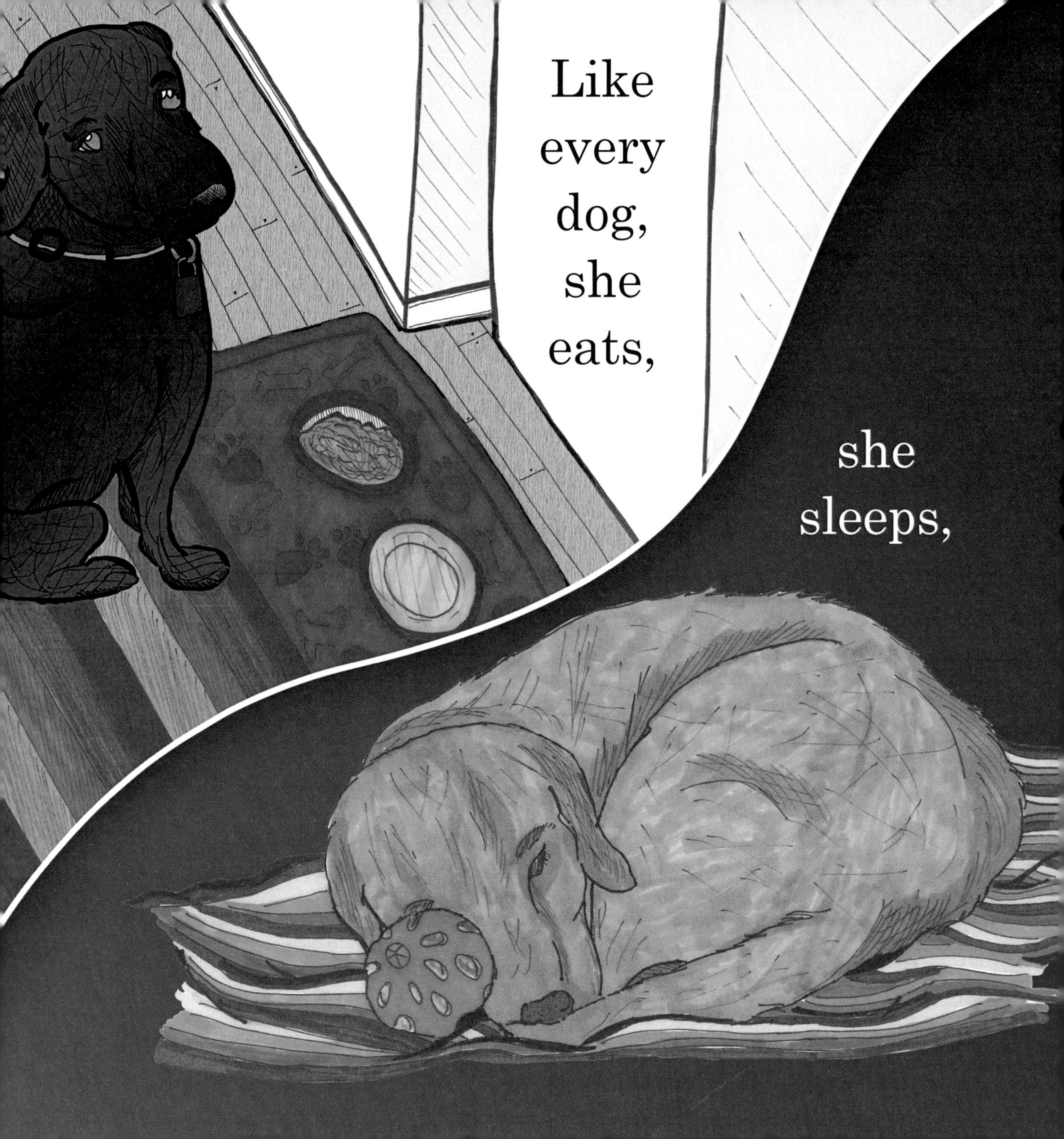
Like
every
dog,
she
eats,
she
sleeps,

and loves us every day."

My friend listened to each word

Attentive and agog

“Now I know what I would be,”

she cheered...

A COURTHOUSE DOG!

CANINE COMPANIONS
FOR INDEPENDENCE

Glossary

~ The Law ~

A series of rules we must live by in order to be good citizens.

~ Courthouse ~

The place where people decide whether we have broken the rules that we must live by.

~ Evidentiary ~

From the word evidence, when someone gives information about something that happened so others can know whether the rules of life have been broken.

~ Witness ~

This is what we call a person who is giving evidence in court.

~ Testify ~

In the courtroom, telling the truth about what you've seen or done is called testifying.

~ Neutrality ~

When someone doesn't take a side.

~ Encroaching ~

Getting in the way.

About Courthouse Dogs Foundation

Mission

Courthouse Dogs Foundation promotes justice with compassion by helping legal professionals successfully implement courthouse facility dog programs using best practices in this field.

Vision

We envision continued growth in the use of courthouse facility dog teams that improve the legal system by helping vulnerable people participate in stressful legal proceedings.

What is a courthouse facility dog?

Courthouse facility dogs are professionally trained dogs working throughout the country in prosecutor's offices, child advocacy centers, and family courts. They primarily provide a calming influence for children during stressful legal proceedings.

As legally neutral companions for witnesses during the investigation and prosecution of crimes, these dogs help the most vulnerable witnesses feel willing and able to describe what happened. The dogs also provide emotional support to participants in family court proceedings and in specialty/treatment courts.

Made in the USA
San Bernardino, CA
14 September 2017